SCOTT JOPLIN
RAGTIME RAGE

COMPILED, ARRANGED AND EDITED BY **JOHN W. SCHAUM** A.S.C.A.P.

SUGGESTIONS for USE of CHORDS - at PIANO and ORGAN

For PIANO: *Right Hand:* Play treble clef melody as written, or in octaves.
Left Hand: Improvise an accompaniment (based on chord symbols).
Consult "Chord Dictionary" on page 16.

For ORGAN: *Upper Manual:* Right hand piays melody as written.
Lower Manual: Left hand improvises and accompaniment (based on chord symbols).
Pedal: Play root of each chord (or - alternate tonic and dominant of each chord).

For CHORD ORGAN or
PIANO ACCORDION: Make the same adjustments as indicated for piano.

BOSWORTH EDITION

The ENTERTAINER

Scott Joplin
Arr. by John W. Schaum
A.S.C.A.P.

EASY WINNERS

Scott Joplin
Arr. by John W. Schaum
A. S. C. A. P.

RAGTIME DANCE

Scott Joplin
Arr. by John W. Schaum
A. S. C. A. P.

MAPLE LEAF RAG

Scott Joplin
Arr. by John W. Schaum
A. S. C. A. P.

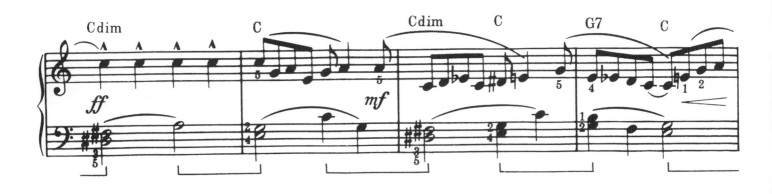

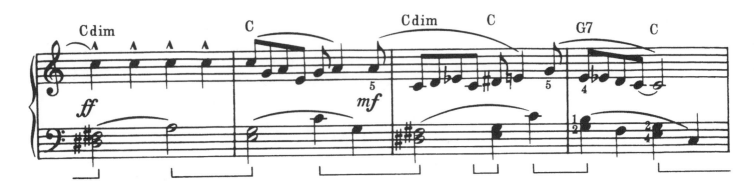

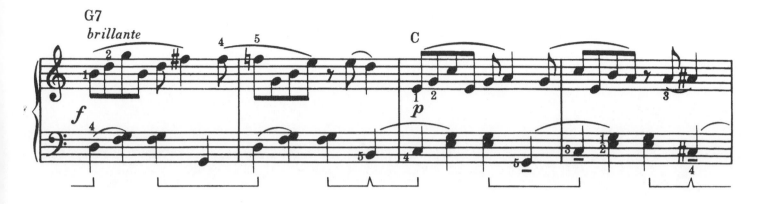

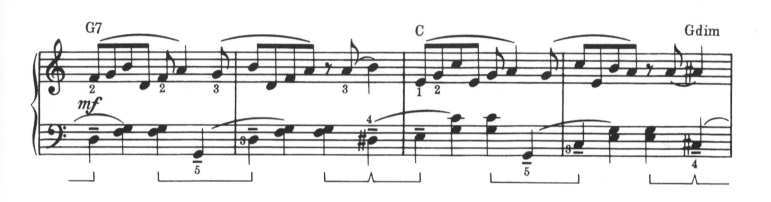

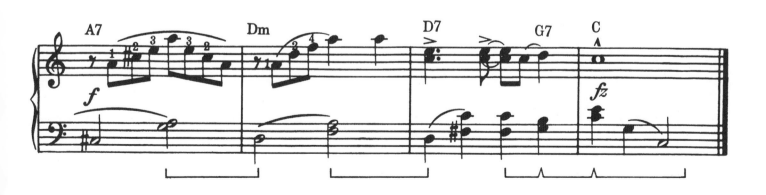

SUNFLOWER SLOW DRAG

Scott Joplin
Arr. by John W. Schaum
A. S. C. A. P.

PEACHERINE RAG

Scott Joplin
Arr. by John W. Schaum
A. S. C. A. P.

13

HELIOTROPE BOUQUET

Scott Joplin
Arr. by John W. Schaum
A. S. C. A. P.

Schaum Chord Dictionary

For F♯ chords use G♭   For G♯ chords use A♭
For C♯ chords use D♭   For D♯ chords use E♭

The letter names of the chords may be rearranged (inverted) if necessary. Example:

PART TWO

ORIGINAL RAGS

Scott Joplin
Arr. by John W. Schaum
A.S.C.A.P.

PALM LEAF RAG

Scott Joplin
Arr. by John W. Schaum
A. S. C. A. P.

✱ Note: Use thumb on both notes

CLEOPHA

Scott Joplin
Arr. by John W. Schaum
A.S.C.A.P.

Andante cantabile

CASCADES

Scott Joplin
Arr. by John W. Schaum
A. S. C. A. P.

25

SYCAMORE RAG

Scott Joplin
Arr. by John W. Schaum
A. S. C. A. P.

ELITE SYNCOPATIONS

Scott Joplin
Arr. by John W. Schaum
A. S. C. A. P.

STRENUOUS LIFE

Scott Joplin
Arr. by John W. Schaum
A.S.C.A.P.

PETER and the WOLF

by SERGE PROKOFIEV
arranged by WESLEY SCHAUM

for PIANO

SCHAUM PUBLICATIONS, INC.

07—75